Designed by Annie Simpson.

Copyright © 2010
make believe ideas ltd
The Wilderness, Berkhamsted, Hertfordshire, HP4 2AZ, UK.
501 Nelson Place, P.O. Box 141000, Nashville, TN 37214-1000, USA.

# The Wheels on the Bus

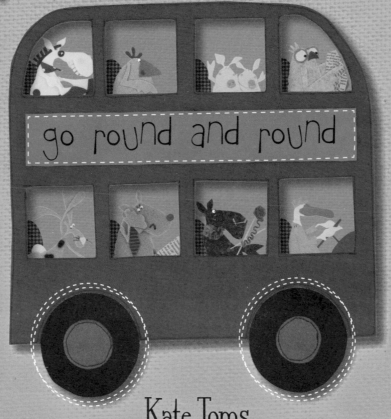

go round and round

Kate Toms

make
believe
ideas

The wheels on the bus go round and round, round and round, round and round.

LIBRARY

The wheels on the bus go round and round, all day long!

go round and round

The **driver** on the bus says,

All aboard,

all aboard,

all aboard.

The **driver** on the bus says,

All aboard,

all day long!

go round and round

The babies on the bus go
wah, wah, wah,
wah, wah, wah,
wah, wah, wah!

The babies on the bus go
wah, wah, wah,

all day long!

go round and round

The grandpas on the bus say,
What's that noise?

What's that noise?

What's that noise?

The grandpas on the bus say,

What's that noise?

all day long!

go round and round

The horn on the bus goes

beep, beep, beep,

beep, beep, beep,

beep, beep, beep.

The horn on the bus goes

beep, beep, beep,

all day long!

go round and round

The **mommies** on the bus go

cluck, cluck, cluck,

cluck, cluck, cluck,

cluck, cluck, cluck.

The **mommies** on the bus go

cluck, cluck, cluck,

all day long!

go round and round

The **children** on the bus jump up and down,
up and down,
up and down.

The **children** on the bus jump up and down,
all day long!

go round and round

LIBRARY

SCHOOL

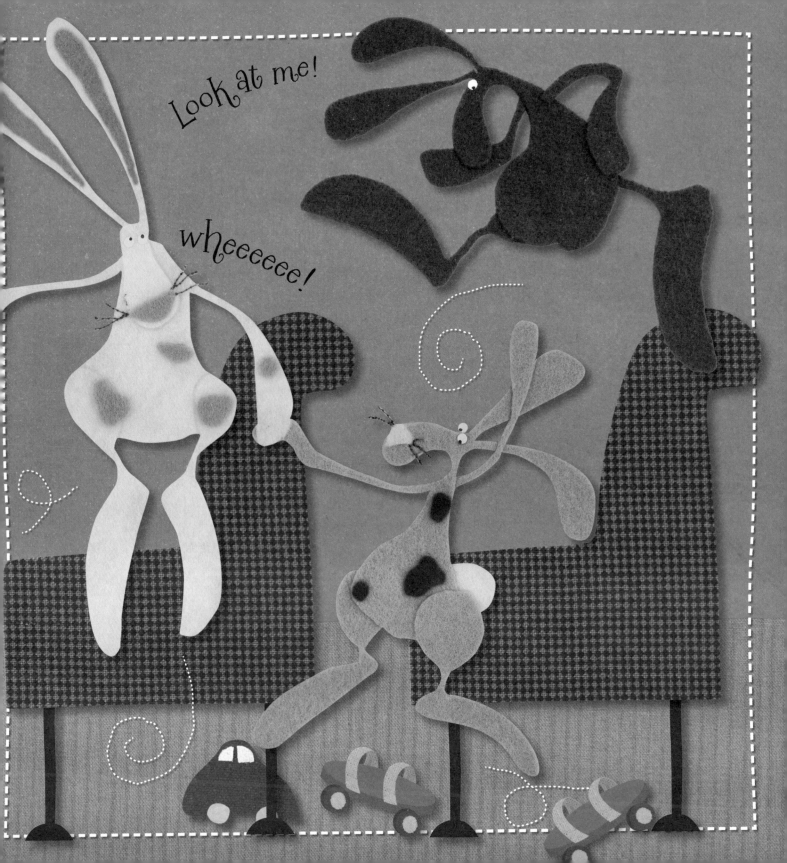

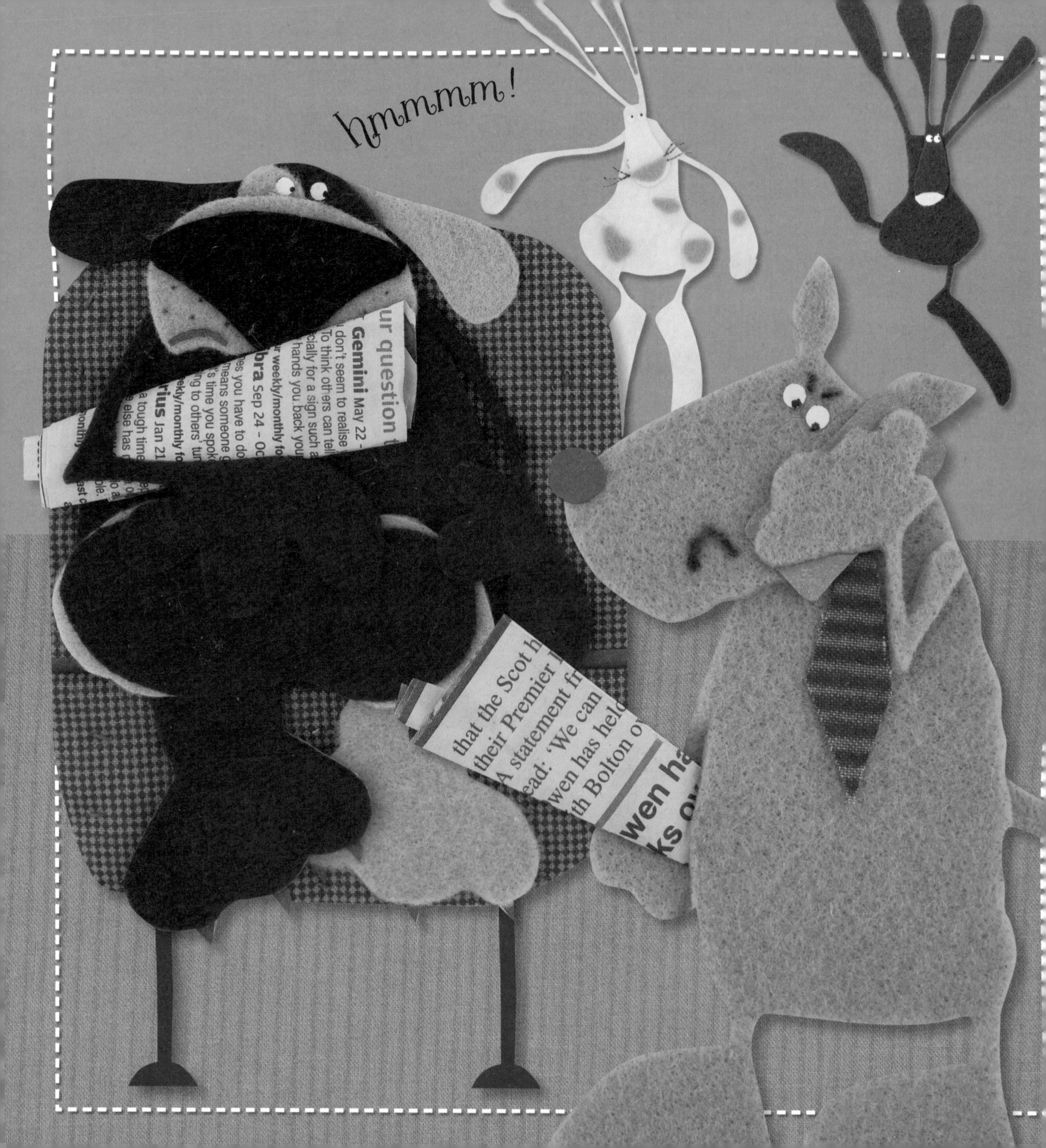
hmmmm!

The **daddies** on the bus say,
Please sit still!
Please sit still!
Please sit still!

The **daddies** on the bus say,
Please sit still!

all day long!

go round and round

The **boys** on the bus just
horse around,
horse around,
horse around.

The **boys** on the bus just
horse around,

all day long!

LAUNDERETTE

go round and round

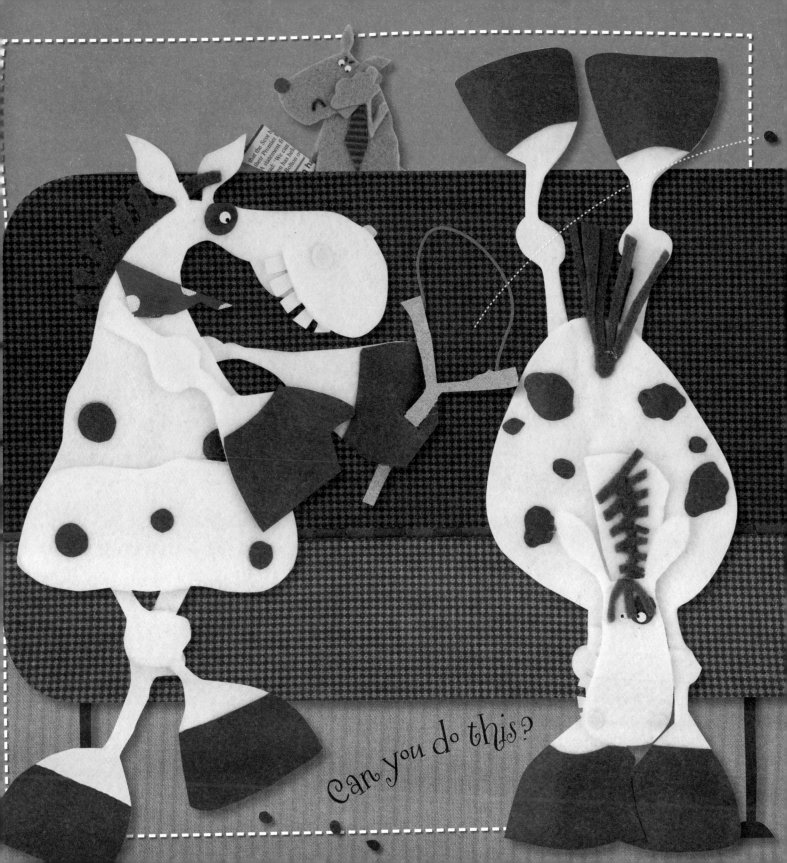

The **bell** on the bus goes

ding, ding, ding,

ding, ding, ding,

ding, ding, ding.

stop

The **bell** on the bus goes

ding, ding, ding,

all day long!

go round and round

The grandmas on the bus go
Knit, Knit, Knit,
Knit, Knit, Knit,
Knit, Knit, Knit.
The grandmas on the bus go
Knit, Knit, Knit,
all day long!

go round and round

The **wheels** on the bus go round and round, round and round, round and round. The **wheels** on the bus go round and round, bye-bye!

all day long!